Written by teachers working in the Canadian classroom

Math
Readiness

K

W9-CST-983

- Counting to 20
- Canadian money, time
- 2D and 3D shapes
- Patterning, classification
- And much more!

Margaret Ann Hawkins, B.Ed.

Kindergarten Math Readiness

Contents

Let's Celebrate Numbers!

1

How many cakes do you see? ☐

Colour the picture.

Trace the number.

Print the number.

Let's Celebrate Numbers!

2

How many balloons do you see? ☐

Trace the number.

2 2 2 2 2 2 2 2 2 2 2

2 2 2 2 2 2 2 2 2 2 2

Print the number.

2

2

Let's Celebrate Numbers!

3

How many pizzas do you see? ☐

Colour the picture.

Trace the number.

3 3 3 3 3 3 3 3 3

3 3 3 3 3 3 3 3 3

Print the number.

3

3

Let's Celebrate Numbers!

4

How many
presents do you see? ☐

Trace the number.

Print the number.

Let's Celebrate Numbers!

5

How many
drinks do you see?

Colour the picture.

Trace the number.

3 →
1 ↓ 5
2 ↻

5 5 5 5 5 5 5 5 5 5 5

5 5 5 5 5 5 5 5 5 5 5 5

Print the number.

5

5

Let's Celebrate Numbers!

6

How many ice cream cones do you see? ☐

Trace the number.

6 6 6 6 6 6 6 6 6 6 6 6

6 6 6 6 6 6 6 6 6 6 6 6

Print the number.

6

6

Let's Celebrate Numbers!

7

How many children do you see? ☐

Colour the picture.

Trace the number.

7 7 7 7 7 7 7 7 7 7

7 7 7 7 7 7 7 7

Print the number.

Let's Celebrate Numbers!

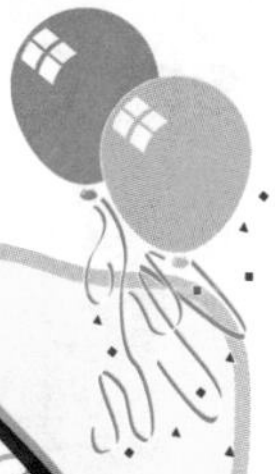

8

How many party hats do you see? ☐

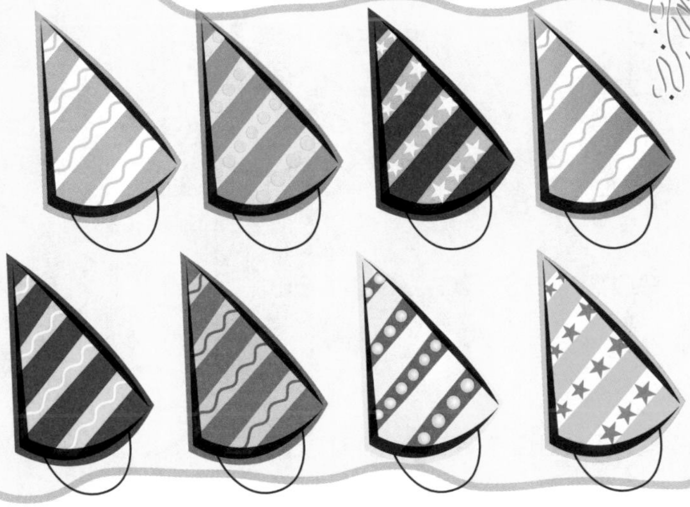

Trace the number.

8 8 8 8 8 8 8 8 8

8 8 8 8 8 8 8 8 8

Print the number.

8

8

Let's Celebrate Numbers!

9

How many candies do you see? ☐

Colour the picture.

Trace the number.

q q q q q q q q q q

q q q q q q q q q q

Print the number.

q

q

Let's Celebrate Numbers!

10

How many bowls of ice cream do you see?

Trace the number.

10 10 10 10 10 10 10

10 10 10 10 10 10

Print the number.

10

10

How Many?

Count the animals in each set.

Circle the correct number.

1 2 3

4 5 6

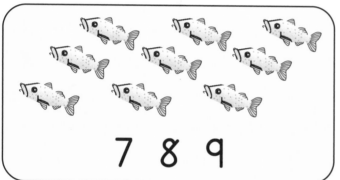

7 8 9

2 3 4

5 6 7

8 9 10

3 4 5

6 7 8

Counting 1 to 10

How many do you see?
Write the number on the line.

 _____

 _____

 _____

 _____

 _____

 _____

 _____

 _____

 _____

 _____

Comparing Numbers

Count and write how many objects are in each group.
Circle the group that has **more**.

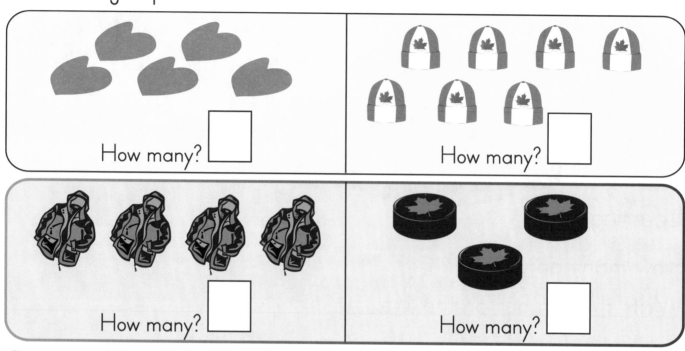

How many? ☐

How many? ☐

How many? ☐

How many? ☐

Count and write how many objects are in each group.
Circle the group that has **less**.

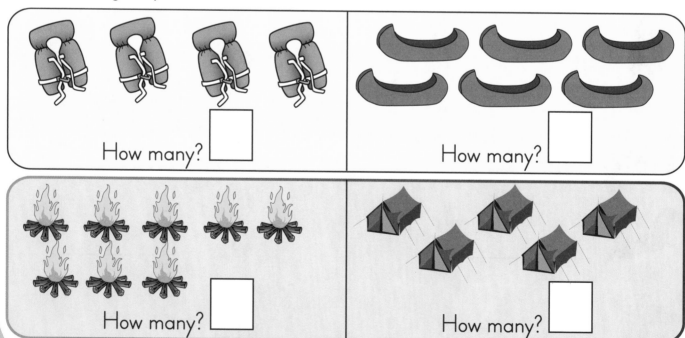

How many? ☐

How many? ☐

How many? ☐

How many? ☐

Comparing Numbers

How many of each object is in each set?
Make the number of objects in each set the same by crossing
out objects.

Number Sequence

0 1 2 3 4 5 6 7 8 9 10

Write the number
that comes **before**.   Example: ___ 3   4   5

___ 3   4

___ 1   2

___ 5   6

___ 2   3

___ 9   10

___ 7   8

___ 6   7

___ 8   9

Number Sequence

0 1 2 3 4 5 6 7 8 9 10

Write the number
that comes **after.**   Example: 1 2 ___3___

3 4 _____

2 3 _____

6 7 _____

5 6 _____

4 5 _____

8 9 _____

7 8 _____

0 1 _____

0 1 2 3 4 5 6 7 8 9 10

Print the numbers 1 to 10 as you paddle down the river to your camp site.

18

Count Down to Blast Off!

Count the items in each row.

Write the number on the line.

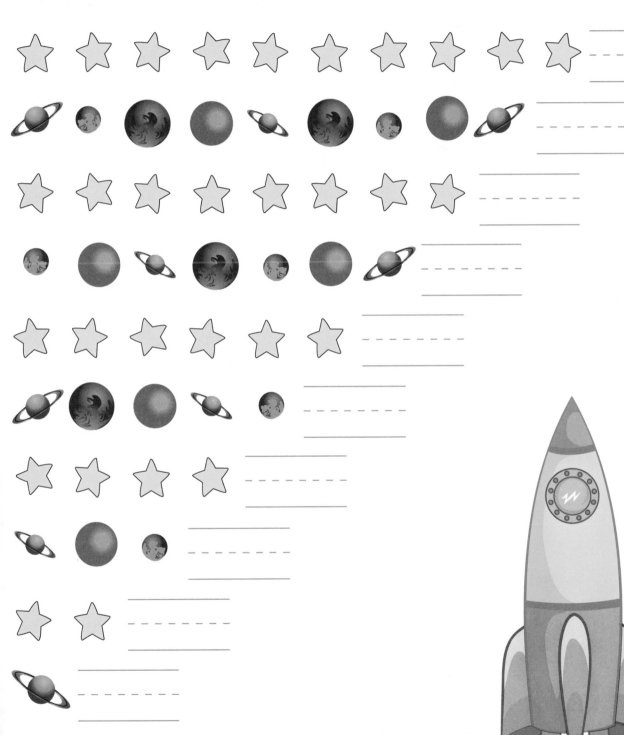

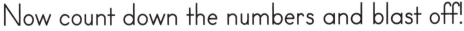

Now count down the numbers and blast off!

Cool Coins

penny	nickel	dime	quarter	dollar	two dollar
1¢	5¢	10¢	25¢	(loonie) $1.00	(toonie) $2.00

Draw a line from the coin to its value.

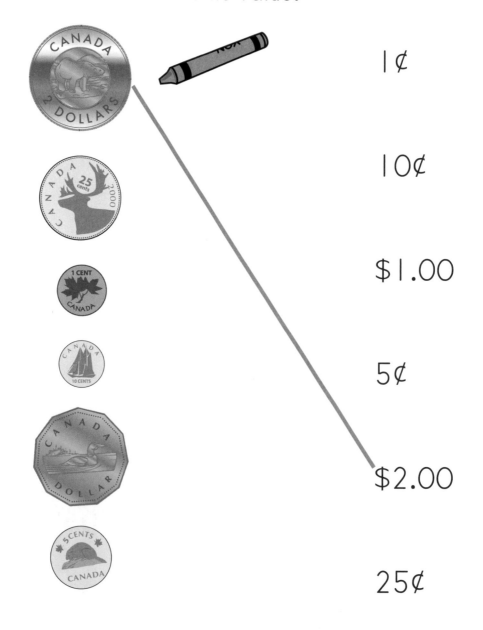

1¢

10¢

$1.00

5¢

$2.00

25¢

Going Shopping

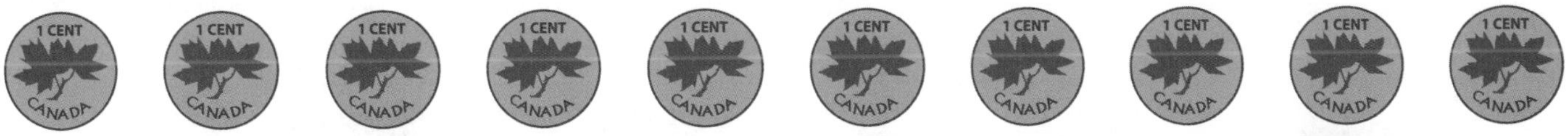

Count the 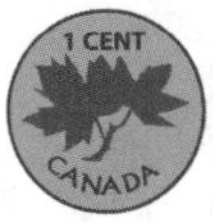. How many? ☐ ¢

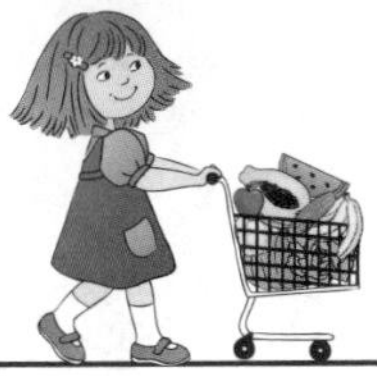

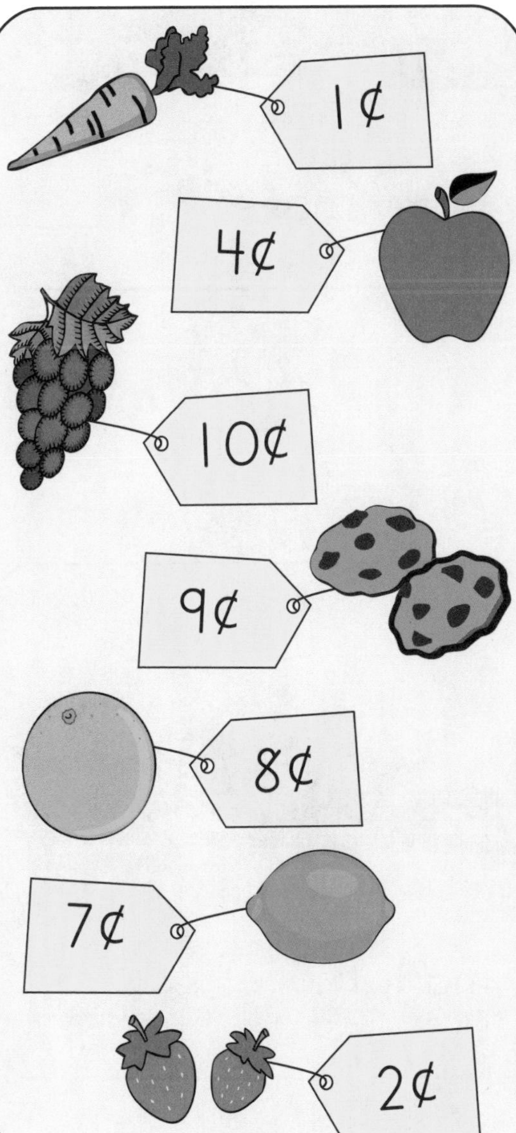

Draw what you could buy.

Put an X on the 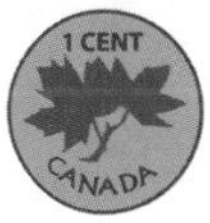 you spend.

How many 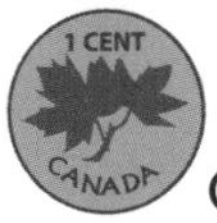 do you have left? Circle the number.

0¢ 1¢ 2¢ 3¢ 4¢ 5¢ 6¢ 7¢ 8¢ 9¢ 10¢

Adding – How Many?

Put an X on each you count.

How many?

How many more?

How many 🌼 are there now?

How many?

How many more?

How many 🐦 are there now?

Subtracting – How Many?

Put an X on each you count.

How many 🍁? ☐

How many 🍁 fell? ☐

Count the 🍁 on the tree.

Now there are ☐ 🍁 on the tree.

How many 🎈? ☐

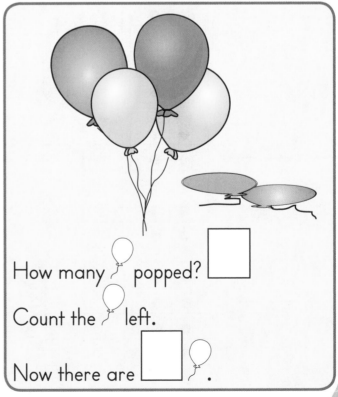

How many 🎈 popped? ☐

Count the 🎈 left.

Now there are ☐ 🎈.

Counting 11 to 20

Trace the number. Count the dots.

Add dots to make the number.

11

12

13

14

15

16

17

18

19

20

Counting 11 to 20

Count the pictures. Circle the matching number.

Hint: Put an **X** on each thing as you count.

One has been started for you.

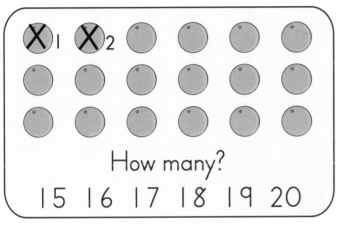

How many?

15 16 17 18 19 20

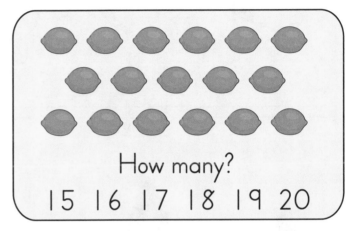

How many?

15 16 17 18 19 20

How many?

15 16 17 18 19 20

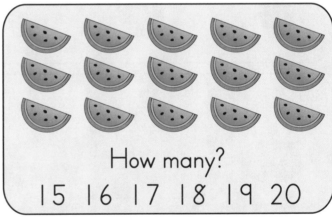

How many?

15 16 17 18 19 20

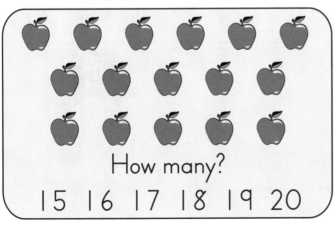

How many?

15 16 17 18 19 20

How many?

15 16 17 18 19 20

Getting Bigger

Draw what is missing.

Measuring with Blocks

How many blocks?

How many blocks long is the paintbrush?

How many blocks long is the eraser?

How many blocks long is the fork?

CRAYON

How many blocks long is the crayon?

Measuring with String

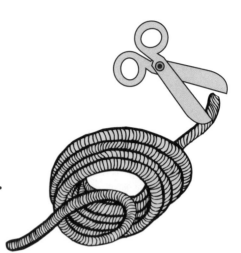

It's Time to Measure!

Cut a piece of string as long as your arm.

Find an object longer than the string.

Find an object the same length as the string.

Find an object shorter than the string.

Draw the objects you found.

Longer than the string.	Same length as the string.	Shorter than the string.

Mass: Is it Heavier or Is it Lighter?

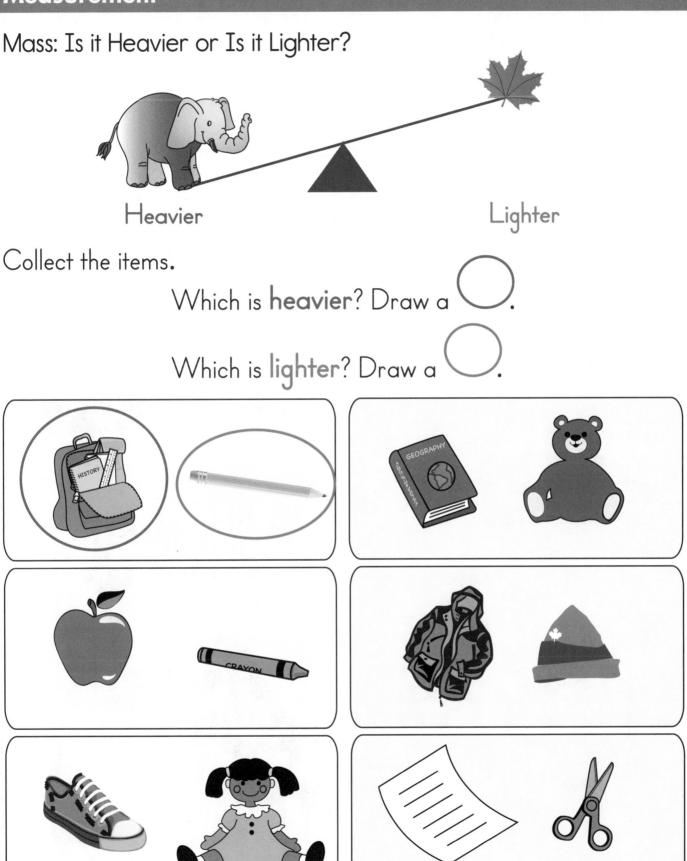

Heavier   Lighter

Collect the items.

Which is **heavier**? Draw a ◯.

Which is **lighter**? Draw a ◯.

Mass: Is it Heavy or Is it Light?

Circle the **heavy** objects in blue.

Circle the light objects in green.

Capacity: How Much Does It Hold?

(Circle) the container that holds the **most**.

Put an **X** on the container that holds the **least**.

Talking about Time

We measure time with a clock.

The big hand tells the minutes. Colour the big hand red.

The little hand tells the hour. Colour the little hand green.

Trace the numbers. Touch each number and say it out loud.

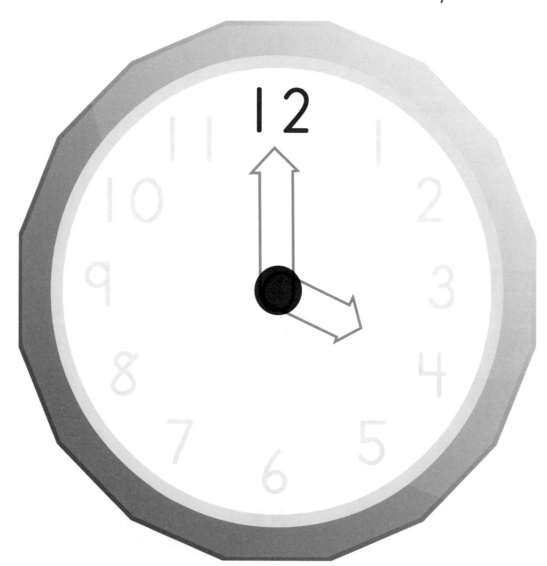

This clock says four o'clock.

My Day – Before and After

Draw what you do **before** school.

Draw what you do **after** dinner.

On Top, Beside, and Under

The pencil case  is on top ⬆ of the desk.

The backpack is beside ➡️⬅️ the desk.

The scissors ✂️ are under ⬇️ the desk.

Count:

How many crayons
under ⬇️ the desk? ☐

How many backpacks
beside ➡️⬅️ the desk? ☐

How many pencils
on top ⬆ the desk? ☐

Super 2-D Shapes

Trace each shape with your finger. Say its name.

circle

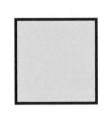

square

triangle

rectangle

Trace the shape.
Draw the shape.

square	triangle

circle	rectangle

Geometry and Spatial Sense

Shape Families

Colour the shapes that belong in each family.

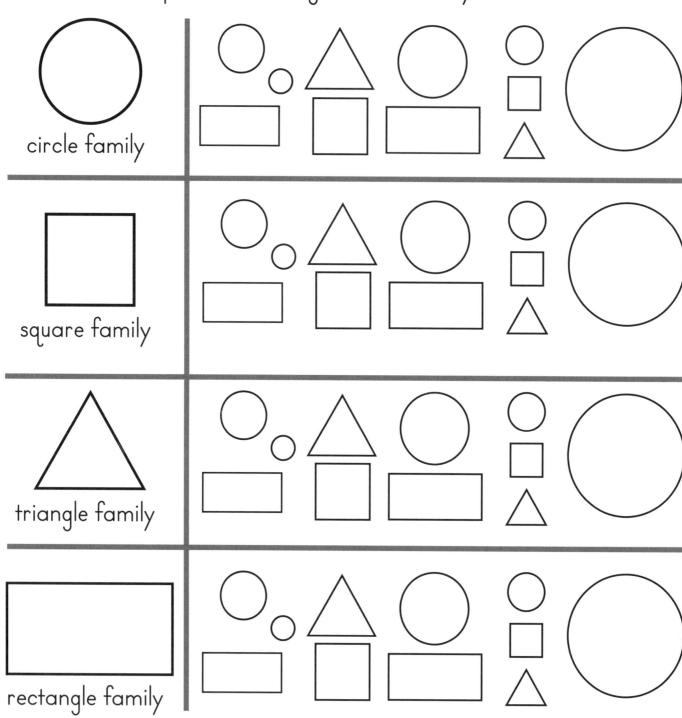

circle family

square family

triangle family

rectangle family

Find the 2-D Shapes

Look at the picture.
Find and count the shapes.

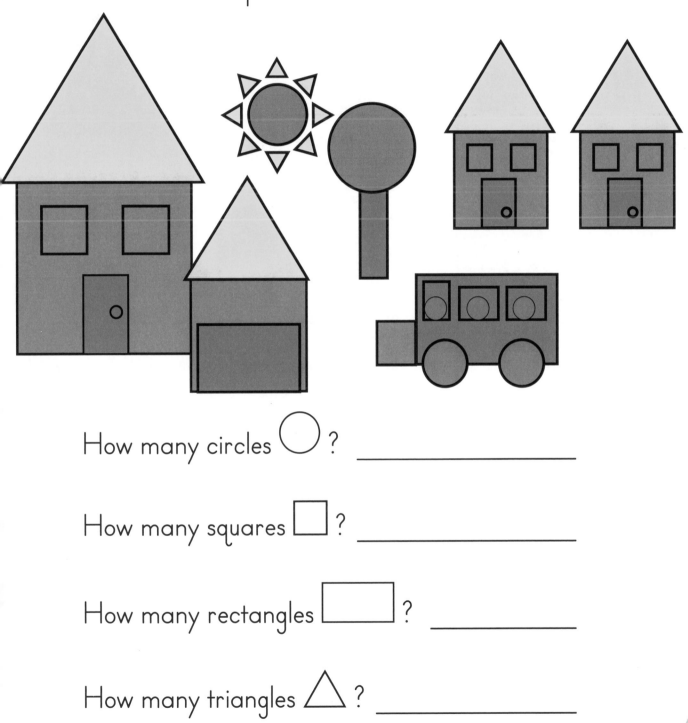

How many circles ◯ ? _____

How many squares ⬜ ? _____

How many rectangles ▭ ? _____

How many triangles △ ? _____

Make a Shape Picture

 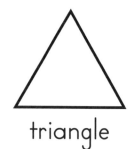 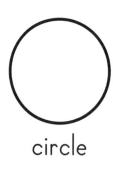 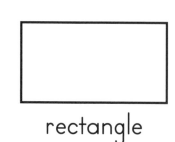

square   circle   triangle   rectangle

Draw a car with shapes

1. Draw a rectangle. 	2. Draw 2 squares on top of the rectangle. 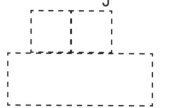	3. Draw a triangle beside one square. 
4. Draw 2 circles under the rectangle. 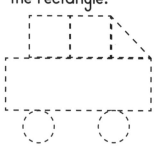	5. Draw 2 more circles inside the squares. 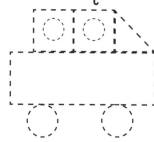	6. Draw 2 small circles at either end of the rectangle. 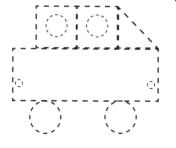

My shape picture has _____ circles ◯.

My shape picture has _____ squares ▢.

My shape picture has _____ triangles △.

My shape picture has _____ rectangles ▭.

3-D Shapes

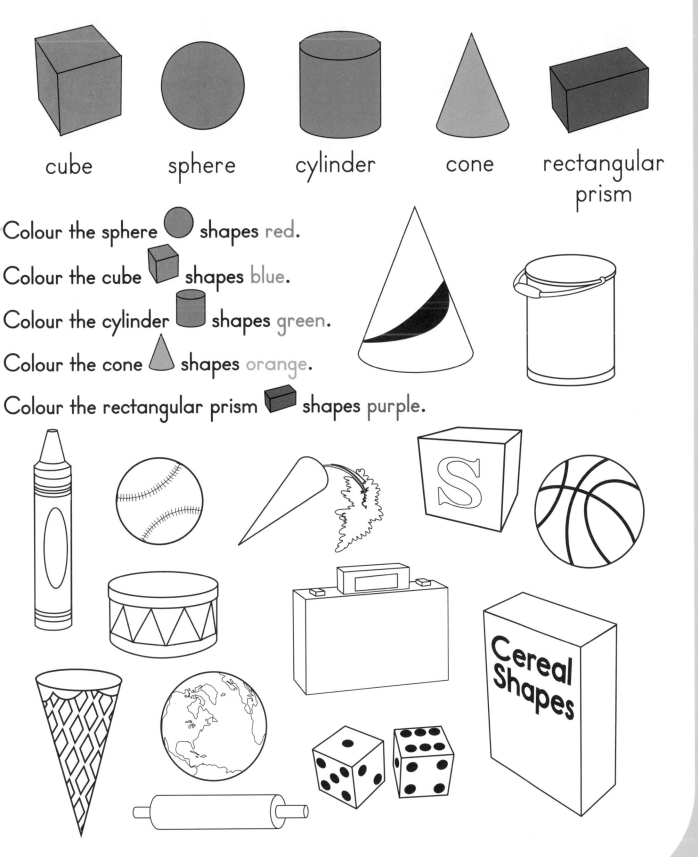

cube   sphere   cylinder   cone   rectangular prism

Colour the sphere shapes red.

Colour the cube shapes blue.

Colour the cylinder shapes green.

Colour the cone shapes orange.

Colour the rectangular prism shapes purple.

Cereal Shapes

Looking for 3-D Shapes

cube   sphere   cylinder   cone   rectangular
                                                              prism

Look for things at home that have these shapes.
Draw what you find.

✔ or ✗

Put a ✔ beside the shape you found the **most** of.

Put an ✗ beside the shape you found the **least** of.

Does it Stack? Does it Roll?

Put a (blue circle) on things that stack. Put a (green circle) on things that roll. Put **both colours** on things that **stack and roll.**

Colour one square blue for each thing that stacks.

Stack:

How many things stack?

Colour one square green for each thing that rolls.

Roll:

How many things roll?

How many things stack and roll?

Patterning

What Comes Next?

A pattern repeats over and over.
Look at this pattern.
Say the name of the shapes.

Say the things in each pattern. Circle what comes next.

What Comes Next?

Say the things in each pattern. Circle what comes next.

Perfect Patterns

Say the things in each pattern. Circle what comes next.

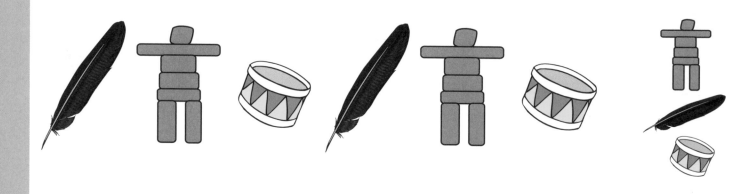

Showing My Patterns Using Letters

We can show patterns in different ways.

Here is a pattern with pictures and letters.

A   B   A   B   A   B   A   B

This is an AB pattern.

Print the letters ABC to show this pattern.

A ___ ___ ___ ___ ___

This is an ABC pattern.

Use letters A B to show this pattern.

___ ___ ___ ___ ___ ___

Action Patterns

Make these patterns by clapping 🖐, snapping ✊, and 👟 stomping.

Try making different action patterns with your hands and feet.
Say the actions in your patterns. Use letters A B C to tell about the
patterns you made. Print the letters to show the patterns you made.

Example:

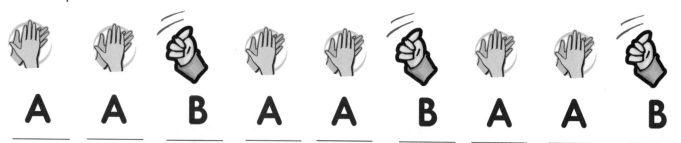

A   A   B   A   A   B   A   A   B

My pattern:

_____   _____   _____   _____

Make Your Own Patterns

Colour the pictures to make patterns.

Use **blue** and yellow. Use A B to show the pattern you made.

____ ____ ____ ____ ____ ____

Use **red** and **blue**. Use A B to show the pattern you made.

____ ____ ____ ____ ____ ____

Choose your own 3 colours to make a pattern. Use A B C to show the pattern you made.

____ ____ ____ ____ ____ ____

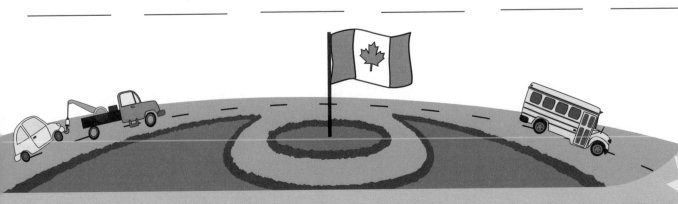

Make Your Own Patterns

Use  to make your own pattern.

Tell what pattern you made.

Patterns are Everywhere!

Look around you. Look for patterns. Look at the patterns on each of these items.

Draw other patterns you see around you.

Look at your favourite shirt.
Does it have a pattern?
Colour the pattern on your shirt.

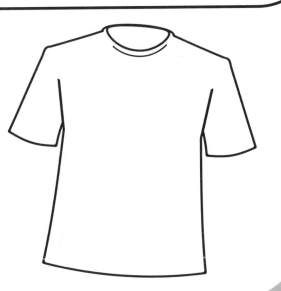

Super Sorting – Same

Circle the ones in each row that are the same.

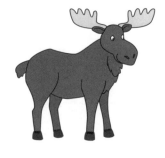   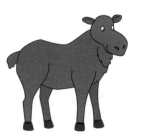

Super Sorting – Different

Sort the fruit. Circle the ones that are different.

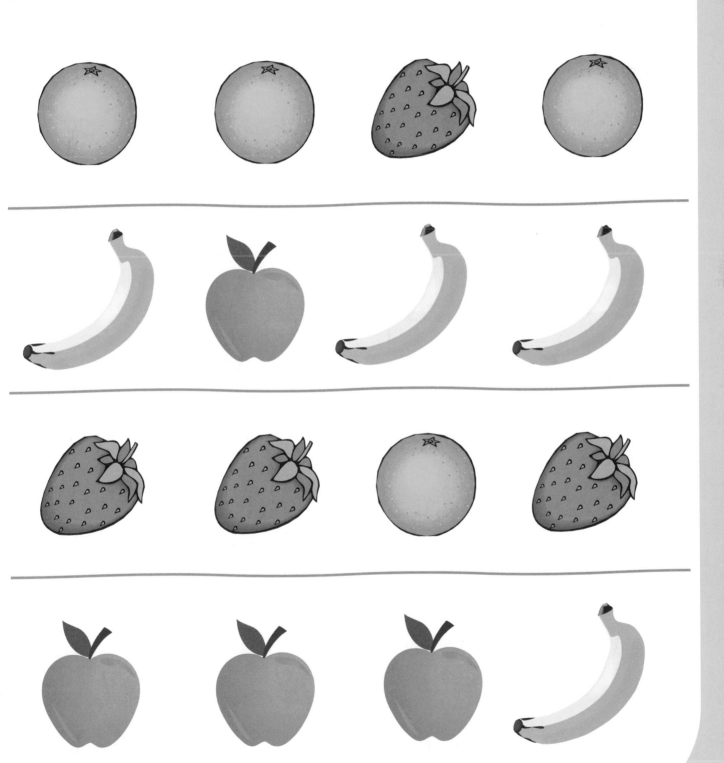

Is it Small, Medium, or Large?

Sort the balloons.

Colour the small balloons your favourite colour.

Put a ✔ on the medium balloons.

Put an X on the large balloons.

What Goes Together?

Circle the pictures in each group that go together.

What Doesn't Belong?

Draw an **X** on the one that doesn't belong.

Graphing: Our Favourite Fruit

A class took a poll to find out everyone's favourite fruit.
How many children chose each kind of fruit?

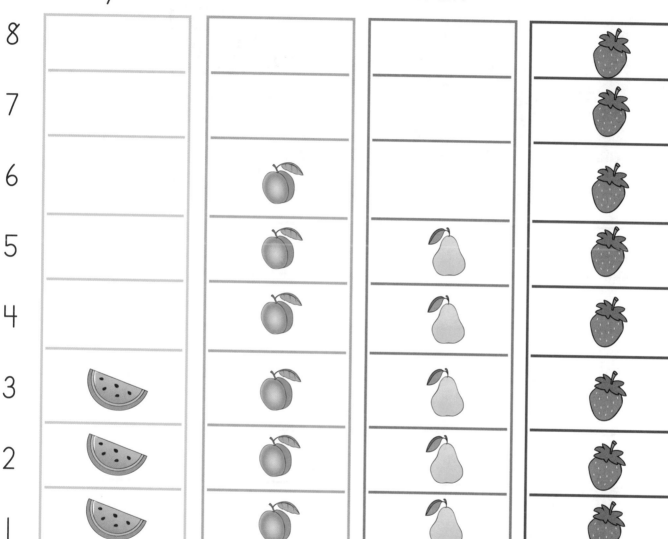

How many ? _____

How many ? _____

How many ? _____

How many ? _____

Circle the **most** popular fruit.

Circle the **least** popular fruit.

Make a Graph

How many of each animal are in the picture?

Colour **one box** for each animal. The is done for you.

7				
6				
5				
4				
3				
2	▨			
1	▨			

Circle the animal there are the most of. Put an **X** on the animal there are the least of.

Heads or Tails?

heads   tails

Flip a penny ten times. On the first graph, colour one box

for each flip to show if it landed **heads** or **tails** .

Then flip it 10 more times and colour the second graph.

Last, flip it 10 more times and colour the third graph.

What do you notice?

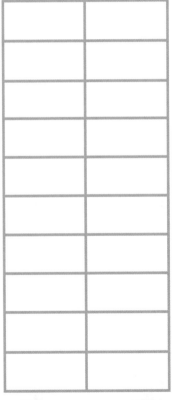   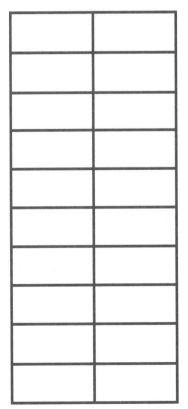   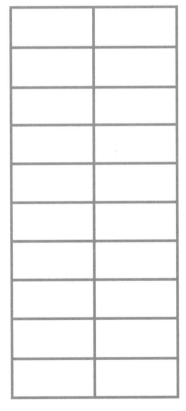

Solutions

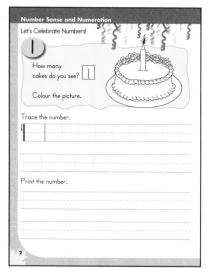

Page 2

Page 3

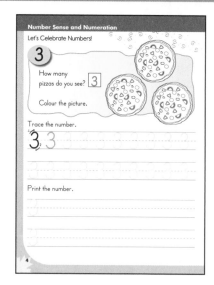

Page 4

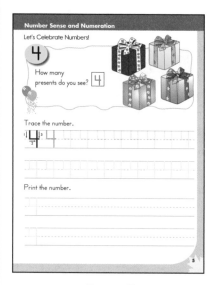

Page 5

Page 6

Page 7

Page 8

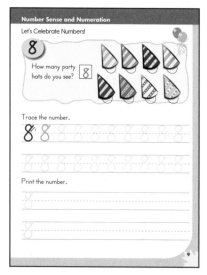

Page 9

Page 10

Solutions

Page 11

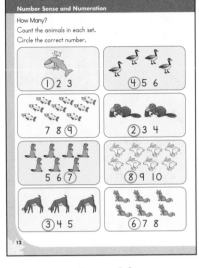

Page 12

Page 13

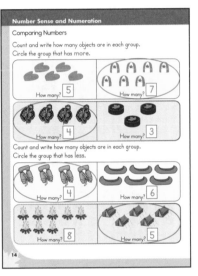

Page 14

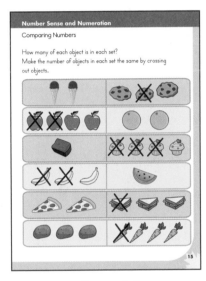

Page 15

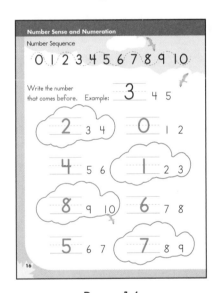

Page 16

Page 17

Page 18

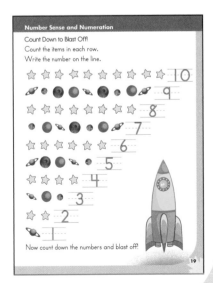

Page 19

Solutions

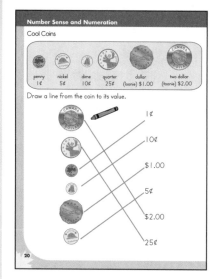

Page 20

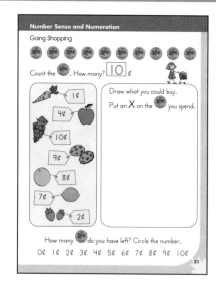

Page 21

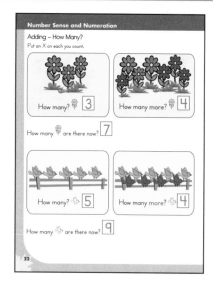

Page 22

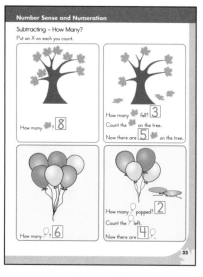

Page 23

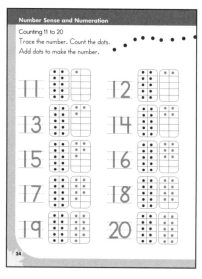

Page 24

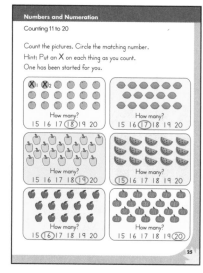

Page 25

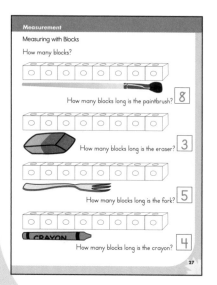

Page 27

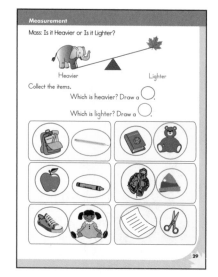

Page 29

Page 30

Solutions

Page 31

Page 34

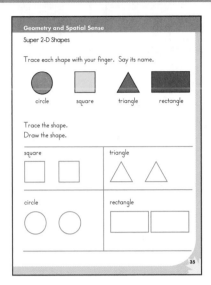

Page 35

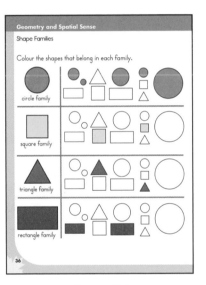

Page 36

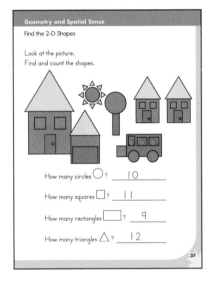

Page 37

Page 39

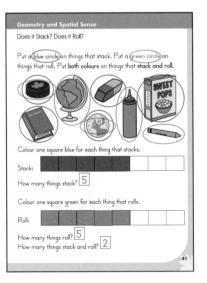

Page 41

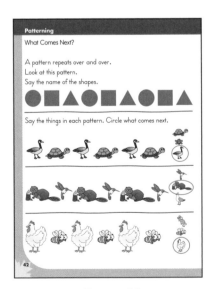

Page 42

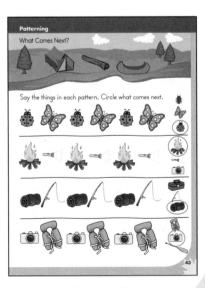

Page 43

Solutions

Page 44

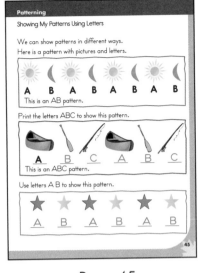

Page 45

Page 50

Page 51

Page 52

Page 53

Page 54

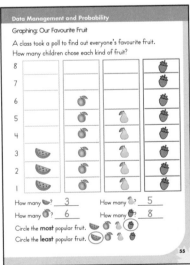

Page 55

Page 56

Data Management and Probability

Heads or Tails?

heads   tails

Flip a penny ten times. On the first graph, colour one box
for each flip to show if it landed **heads** or **tails**.
Then flip it 10 more times and colour the second graph.
Last, flip it 10 more times and colour the third graph.
What do you notice?   Answers will vary.

57

Page 57

Kindergarten Reading Readiness

Contents

Ss Print S and s.

Šš SSSSSS

ŝš SSSSSS

Look at the pictures. Print the beginning letter on each word. Read the word.

s tar

___pider

___poon

___wing

Aa Print A and a.

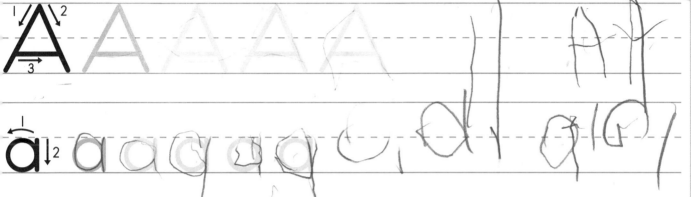

Colour the pictures. Print the beginning letter on each word. Read the word.

___nt

___stronaut

___pple

___rrow

3

T t   Print T and t.

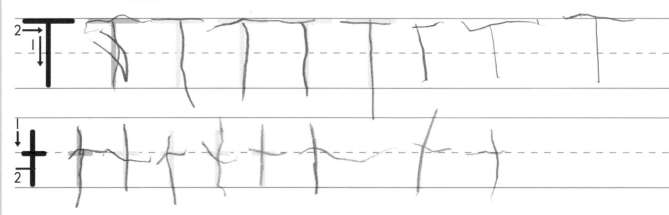

Look at the pictures. Print the beginning letter on each word. Read the word.

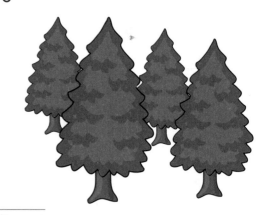

 Teapot

Trees

 Tent

Table

I i Print I and i.

Colour the pictures. Print the beginning letter on each word. Read the word.

____ gloo

____ nsect

____ ce cream

____ ron

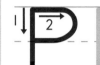 Print **P** and **p**.

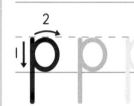

P P P P P

p p p p p p

Look at the pictures. Print the beginning letter on each word. Read the word.

___ig

___ear

___umpkin

___izza

N n Print N and n.

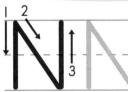

N N N N N

n n n n n n n n

Colour the pictures. Print the beginning letter on each word. Read the word.

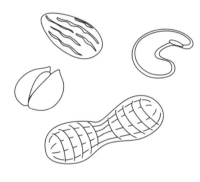

___ e s t

___ u t s

9

___ o s e

___ i n e

Cc Kk Print C and c, K and k.

C C C C C C

K K K K K K

c c c c   k k k k

Look at the pictures. Print the beginning letter on each word. Read the word.

___ up

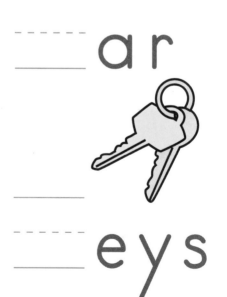

___ ar

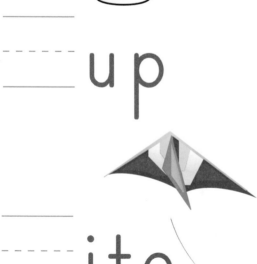

___ ite

___ eys

Cut out the letters at the bottom. Glue the letters to finish the words. Read the words you made.

tar

ron

nt

ig

ree

est

a i n s p t

Connect the Dots

Start
a

Space for cutting on reverse side of page.

E e   Print **E** and **e**.

E E E E E E

e e e e e e e

Colour the pictures. Print the beginning letter on each word. Read the word.

___lbow

___ar

___lephant

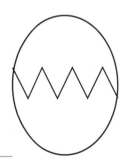

___gg

Hh Print H and h.

Look at the pictures. Print the beginning letter on each word. Read the word.

_____ at

_____ ouse

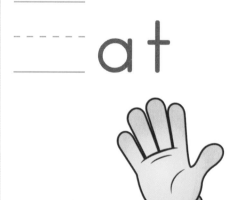

_____ and

_____ orse

Rr Print R and r.

R R R R R R

r r r r r r

Colour the pictures. Print the beginning letter on each word. Read the word.

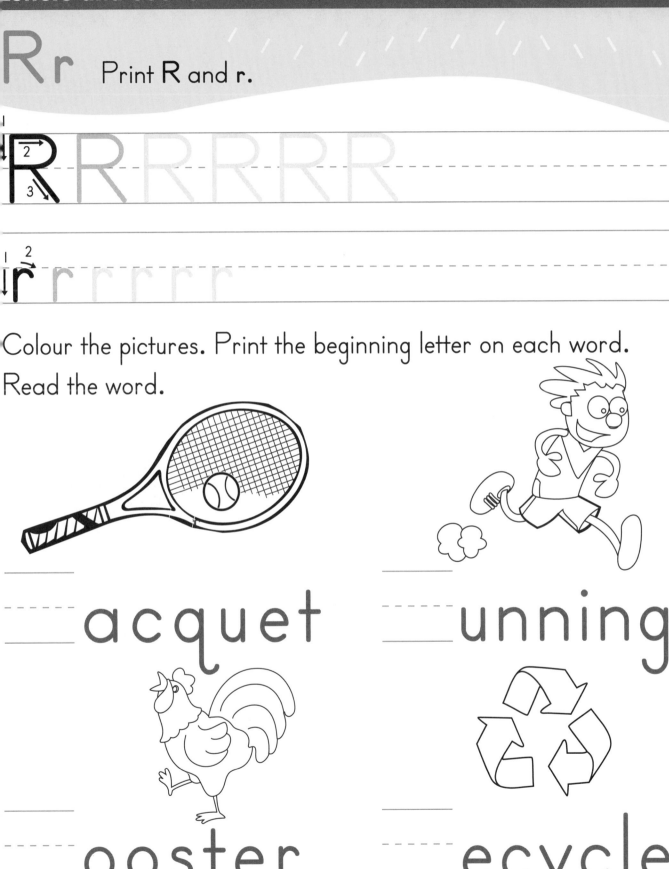

____acquet

____unning

____ooster

____ecycle

13

Mm Print M and m.

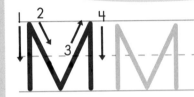

M M M M M M

m m m m m

Look at the pictures. Print the beginning letter on each word. Read the word.

___ oon

___ ittens

___ om

___ uffin

Dd Print D and d.

D D D D D D

d d d d d d

Look at the pictures. Print the beginning letter on each word. Read the word.

___ olphin

___ ress

___ rum

___ og

 Print G and **g**.

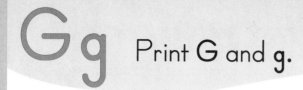

Look at the pictures. Print the beginning letter on each word.
Read the word.

_____ rapes

_____ oat

_____ host

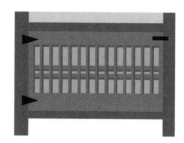

_____ ate

Making Words

Cut out the letters at the bottom. Glue the letters to finish the words. Read the words you made.

ar

gg

orse

abbit

oon

rum

c h d r e m

Connect the Dots

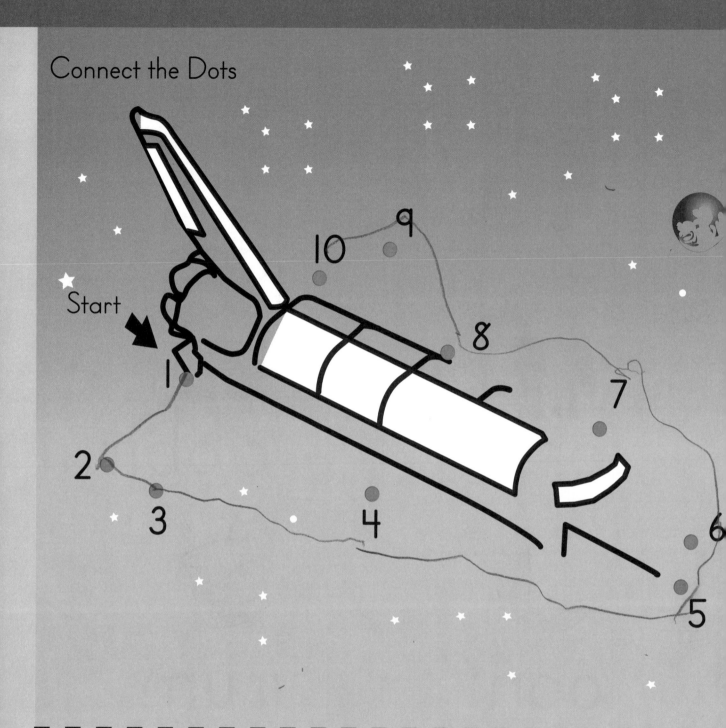

Start

1
2
3
4
5
6
7
8
9
10

Space for cutting on reverse side of page.

18

O o   Print **O** and **o**.

Colour the pictures. Print the beginning letter on each word.
Read the word.

range   nion

n /   ff

19

U u Print U and u.

Look at the pictures. Print the beginning letter on each word.
Read the word.

___mbrella

___dder

___p

___nicorn

Ll Print L and l.

Look at the pictures. Print the beginning letter on each word. Read the word.

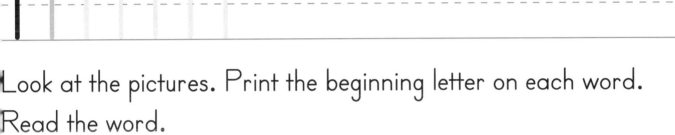

_emon

_ollipop

_ips

_eaf

F f   Print F and f.

Look at the pictures. Print the beginning letter on each word.
Read the word.

___ lag

___ ire

___ ish

___ eather

Bb   Print B and b.

B B B B B B

b b b b b b

Colour the pictures. Print the beginning letter on each word.
Read the word.

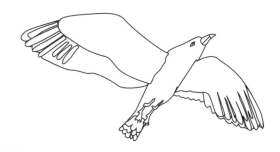

_____ ird

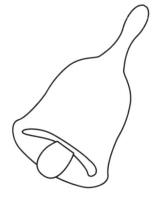

_____ ell

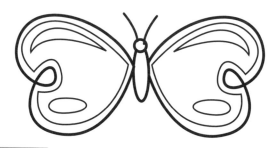

_____ utterfly

_____ all

23

Jj

Print J and j.

J J J J J J J

j j j j j j j

Look at the pictures. Print the beginning letter on each word.
Read the word.

___acket

___ump

___am

___uice

Making Words

Cut out the letters at the bottom. Glue the letters to finish the words. Read the words you made.

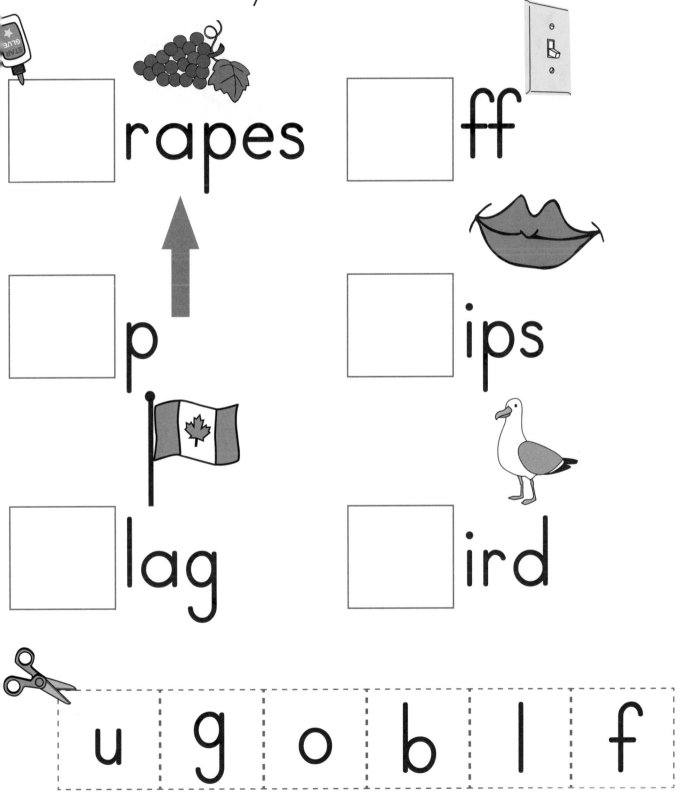

rapes

ff

p

ips

lag

ird

u g o b l f

Follow the dots from 1 to 10.
Colour the picture.

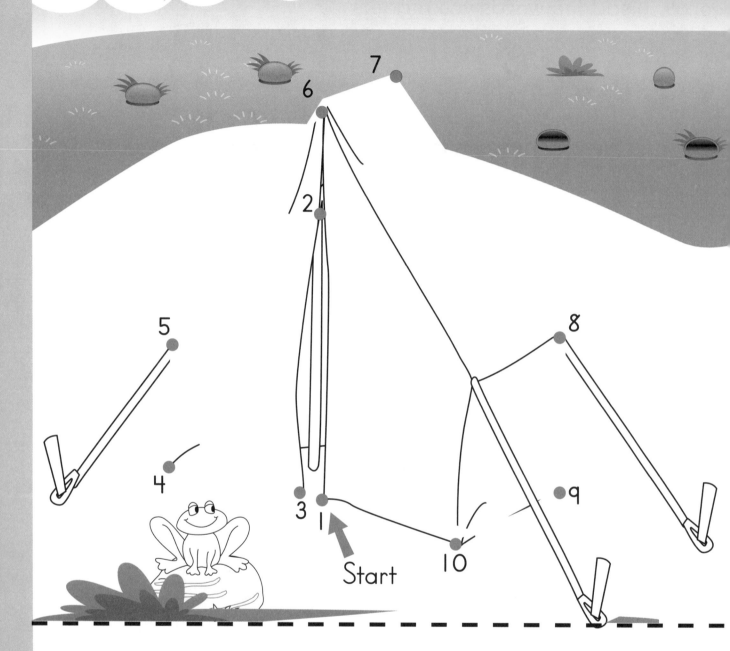

7

6

2

5

8

4

3 1

9

Start

10

Space for cutting on reverse side of page.

Z z   Print **Z** and **z**.

Z Z Z Z Z Z

Z Z Z Z Z Z

Colour the pictures. Print the beginning letter on each word. Read the word.

___ ebra

O

___ ero

___ ig ___ ag

___ oo

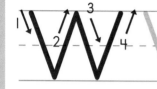 Print W and w.

Look at the pictures. Print the beginning letter on each word. Read the word.

_ _ _ _ _ atermelon   _ _ _ _ _ eb

_ _ _ _ _ ings   _ _ _ _ _ orm

28

V v   Print V and v.

V V V V V V V

v v v v v v v

Colour the pictures. Print the beginning letter on each word.
Read the word.

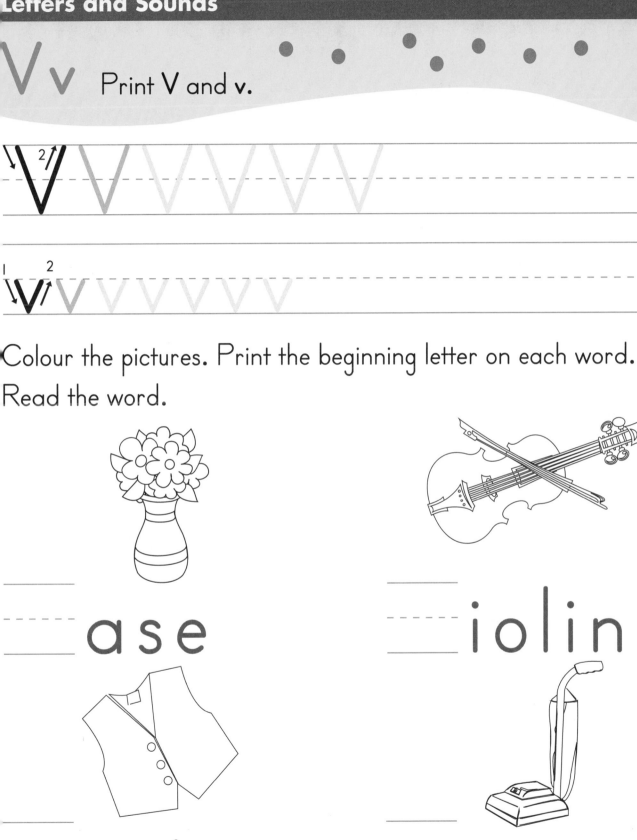

___ ase

___ iolin

___ est

___ acuum

Y y Print Y and y.

Y Y Y Y Y Y Y

y y y y y y y

Look at the pictures. Print the beginning letter on each word.
Read the word.

____ o-yo

____ arn

____ am

____ ogurt

Xx Print X and x.

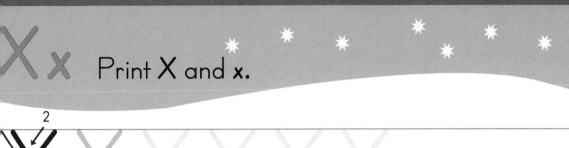

Colour the pictures. Print the **beginning or ending** letters on each word. Read the word.

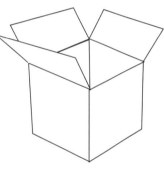

fo___

bo___

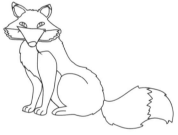

___ray

si___

CH ch Print CH and ch.

CH CH CH

ch ch ch

Look at the pictures. Print the beginning letters on each word.
Read the word.

_____oo _____oo train

_____icken

_____eese

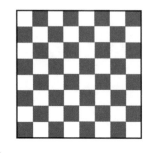

_____ecker board

Making Words

Cut out the letters at the bottom. Glue the letters to finish the words. Read the words you made.

am

O ero

eb

est

arn

fo

j   v   w   z   x   y

Follow the dots from 1 to 10.
Colour the picture.

10
9
8
7
6
4
2
3
5
Start
1

Space for cutting on reverse side of page.

SH sh Print SH and sh.

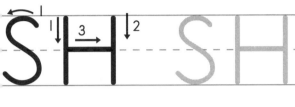

SH SH

sh sh sh

Colour the pictures. Print the beginning letters on each word. Read the word.

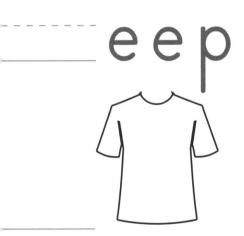

_____ eep

_____ irt

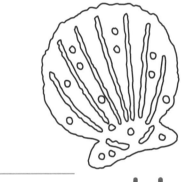

_____ ell

_____ oe

TH th   Print **TH** and **th**.

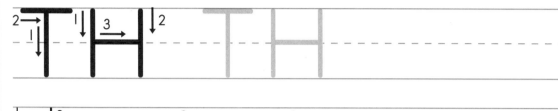

Look at the pictures. Print the beginning or ending letters on each word. Read the word.

___ imble

___ ree

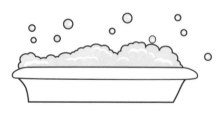

ba ___

tee ___

QU qu   Print **QU** and **qu**.

QU QU QU

qu qu qu

Colour the pictures. Print the beginning letters on each word. Read the word.

_____ e e n

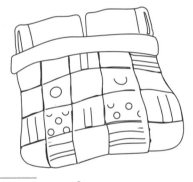

_____ i l t

_____ a r t e r

_____ a c k

ING ing

Print **ING** and **ing**.

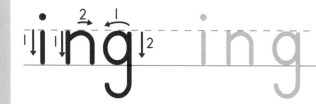

Look at the pictures. Print the ending letters on each word.
Read the word.

swing ____

see ____

runn ____

play ____

ER er Print **ER** and **er**.

e r er er

Look at the pictures. Print the ending letters on each word. Read the word.

ski_____

scoot_____

surf_____

flow_____

 Print **AR** and **ar**.

 AR

 ar ar

Look at the pictures. Print the missing letters on each word.
Read the word.

s t _____

b __ k

c _____

c __ t

Making Words

Cut out the letters at the bottom. Glue the letters to finish the words. Read the words you made.

☐ eese

☐ ell

3 ☐ ree

☐ een

flow ☐

st ☐

ch | sh | th | er | ar | qu

Colour me!

- -

Space for cutting on reverse side of page.

Rhyming Helps Me Read

 **at** word family

This is a cat.

See how many words you can make that rhyme with **cat.**

Print the beginning letter to make the word.

Read the words you made.

c s r b h p m f

c at   __ at

__ at   __ at

__ at   __ at

__ at   __ at

Rhyming Helps Me Read

an word family

This is a **fan**.

See how many words you can make that rhyme with **fan.**
Print the beginning letter to make the word.
Read the words you made.

f b c p r t v m

f a n   ___ a n

___ a n   ___ a n

___ a n   ___ a n

___ a n   ___ a n

Rhyming Helps Me Read

en word family

This is a hen.

See how many words you can make that rhyme with hen.

Print the beginning letter to make the word.

Read the words you made.

h d m p t

h e n

10

___ e n   ___ e n

___ e n   ___ e n

Rhyming Helps Me Read

word family

This is a nut.

See how many words you can make that rhyme with **nut.**
Print the beginning letter to make the word.
Read the words you made.

n g b h c r

n u t   _ u t

_ u t   _ u t

_ u t   _ u t

Rhyming Helps Me Read

ot word family

This is a pot.

See how many words you can make that rhyme with **pot**.

Print the beginning letter to make the word.

Read the words you made.

p g h d l n c r

___ p o t   ___ o t

___ o t   ___ o t

___ o t   ___ o t

___ o t   ___ o t

Rhyming Helps Me Read

ap word family

This is a cap.

See how many words you can make that rhyme with **cap.**
Print the beginning letter to make the word.
Read the words you made.

c   r   g   l   m   n   s   t

_c_ ap	___ ap
___ ap	___ ap
___ ap	___ ap
___ ap	___ ap

Rhyming Helps Me Read

word family

This is a net.

See how many words you can make that rhyme with **net.**

Print the beginning letter to make the word.

Read the words you made.

n b j g m l p s

n e t	___ e t
___ e t	___ e t
___ e t	___ e t
___ e t	___ e t

Rhyming Helps Me Read  **in** | word family

This is a pin.

See how many words you can make that rhyme with pin.
Print the beginning letter to make the word.
Read the words you made.

p w t f b k

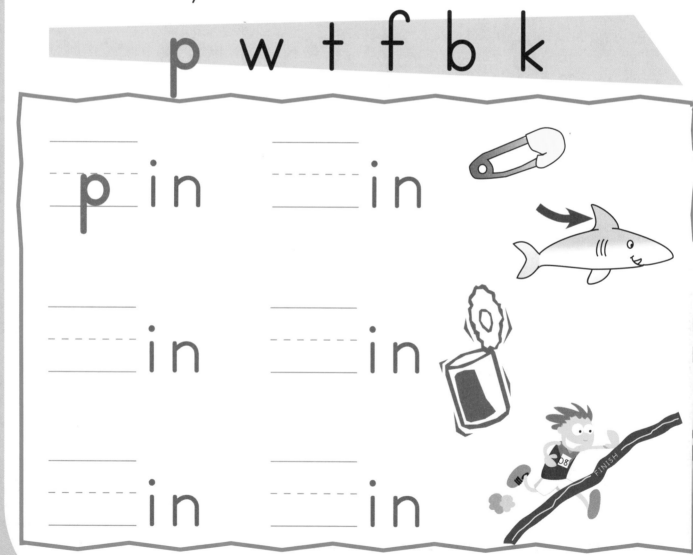

p in   ___ in

___ in   ___ in

___ in   ___ in

Rhyming Helps Me Read **it** **word family**

See the dog sit.

See how many words you can make that rhyme with **sit.**

Print the beginning letter to make the word.

Read the words you made.

k b s h p

s i t

___ i t

___ i t

___ i t

___ i t

Super Sight Words

These words will help you when you read.
Read each word. Draw a line to the matching word.

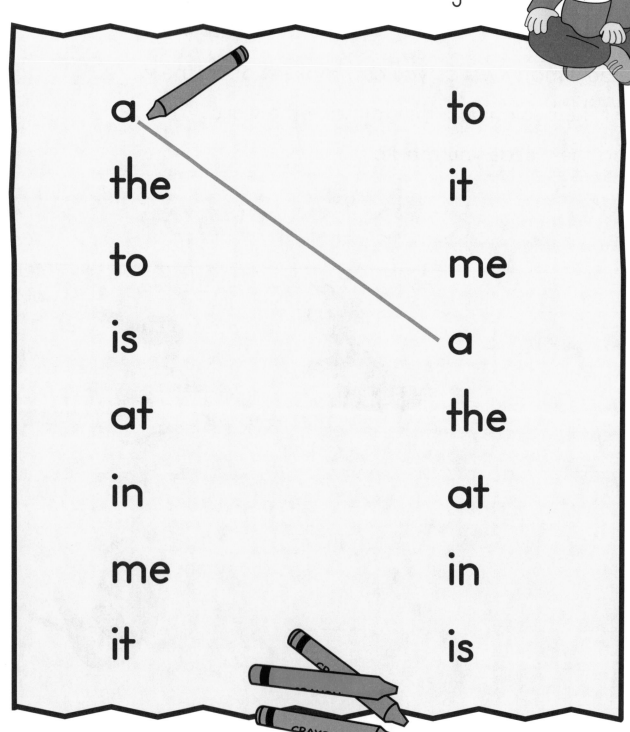

a

the

to

is

at

in

me

it

to

it

me

a

the

at

in

is

Super Sight Words

These words will help you when you read.
Read each word. Draw a line to the matching word.

Mom	love
Dad	girl
love	went
boy	Mom
girl	boy
went	look
play	play
look	Dad

Reading Colour Words

Colour each balloon the colour is says on it.

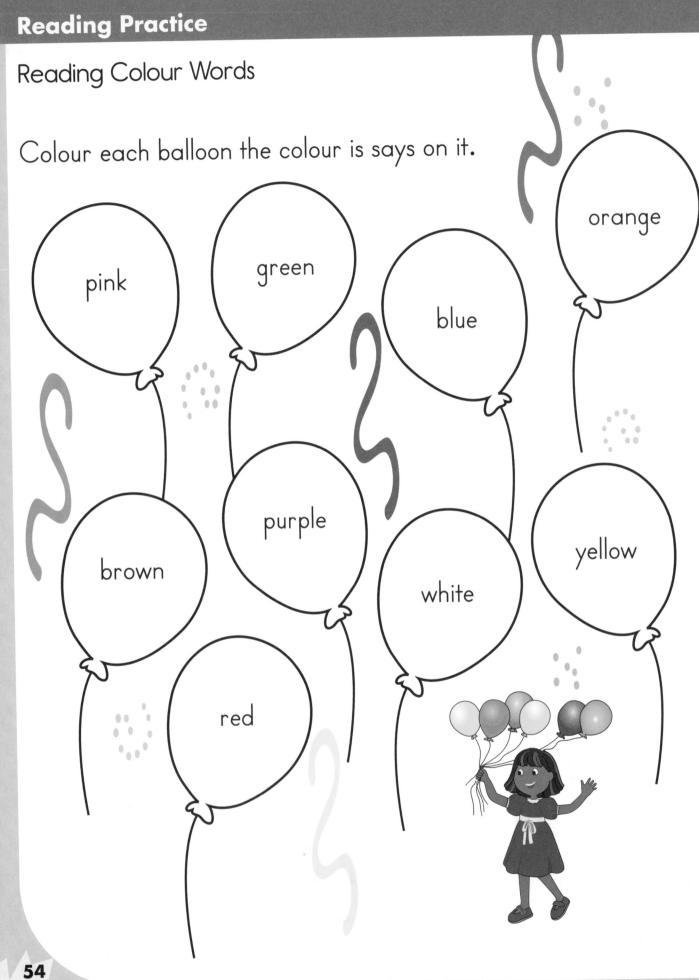

orange

pink

green

blue

purple

brown

yellow

white

red

Reading Number Words

1	2	3	4	5	6	7	8	9	10
one	two	three	four	five	six	seven	eight	nine	ten

Connect the dots from one to ten.

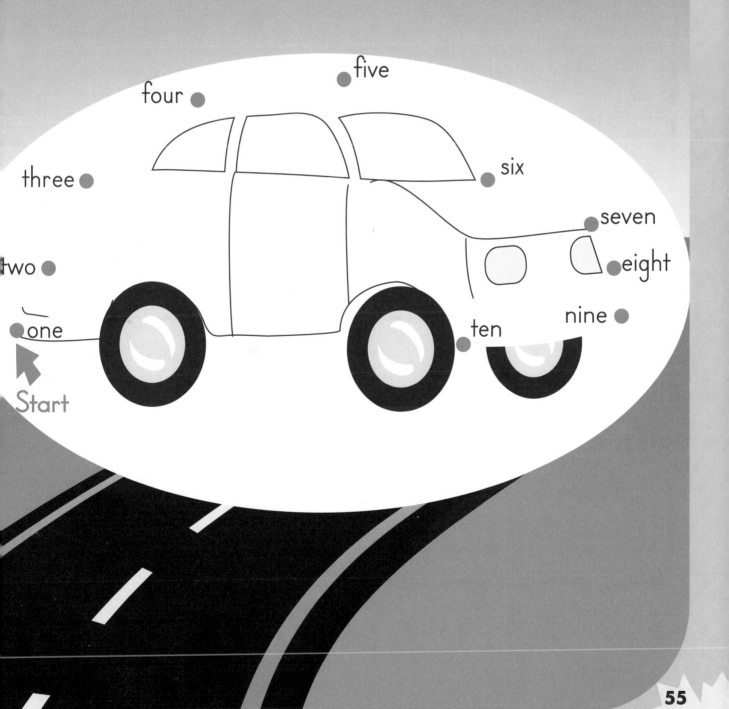

Read and Draw

Read the sentence.
Draw and colour a picture to go with each sentence.

He is at the playground.

She is in the pool.

Read and Draw

Read the sentence.
Draw and colour a picture to go with each sentence.

The rainbow is in the sky.

I have my umbrella in the rain.

57

Reading Practice

It's Time to Read

Read the sentence.
Draw a line to match each sentence to a picture.

I see the slide.

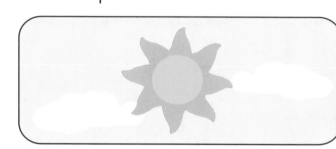

The cat is orange.

He is at the park.

The sun is in the sky.

I am 5 years old.

It's Time to Read

Read the sentence.

Draw a line to match each sentence to a picture.

I see an apple.

The dog is black.

She is a girl.

The car is green.

It is raining.

It's Time to Read

Look at the picture.
Read the sentence. Print the missing word.

The bird ——— flying.

The ——— is in the house.

I like ——— swim.

I ——— fly a kite

can   is   dog   to

Nursery Rhyme Time

Read the nursery rhyme.

Write the numbers 1, 2, 3, 4 to put the rhyme in order.

Hickory, Dickory, Dock

The clock struck one.

bong

The mouse ran down.
Hickory, dickory, dock.

Hickory, dickory, dock

The mouse ran up the clock.

Nursery Rhyme Time

Read the nursery rhyme.

Write the numbers 1, 2, 3, 4 to put the rhyme in order.

Jack and Jill

And Jill came tumbling after.

Jack fell down and broke his crown.

Jack and Jill went up the hill.

To fetch a pail of water.

Nursery Rhyme Time

Read the nursery rhyme.

Write the numbers 1, 2, 3, 4 to put the rhyme in order.

Little Miss Muffet

Along came a spider and sat down beside her.

Little Miss Muffet sat on a tuffet.

1

Eating her curds and whey.

And frightened Miss Muffet away.

Words to Learn

Here is a list of high frequency sight words for children to learn to read by Grade 1.

Practice these early in the Kindergarten year.

a	he	love	out
an	I	me	see
and	in	mom	so
can	it	my	the
dad	like	no	to
			you

These are more words for children to learn by Grade 1.
Practice these later in the Kindergarten year.

am	day	let	she
at	do	look	stop
be	go	one	two
because	good	red	up
black	green	ran	we
blue	is	say	while
by			yes

Kindergarten Writing Readiness

Contents

Getting Ready For Writing

Use your finger, then a pencil, to follow each pet to its home.

Getting Ready For Writing

Use your finger, then a pencil, to help each animal find its home.

3

Getting Ready For Writing

Use your finger, then a pencil, to drive
each vehicle on the road to the garage.
Don't touch the sides of the road!

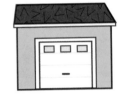

Getting Ready For Writing

Draw curved lines to the pencil cases
with your finger then a pencil.
Don't touch the lines!

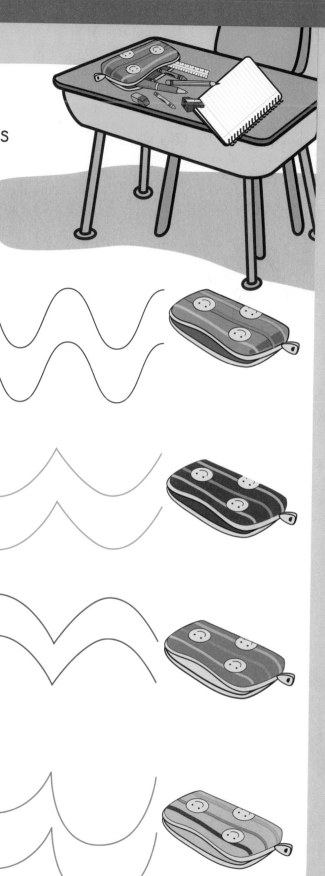

Printing and Letter Sounds

Start

Follow the arrows with your finger, then a pencil.

Trace and print A and a. Say the letter sound.

A A A A A A A A A

A

a a a a a a a a a a

a

Circle the things that start with a.

airplane

apple

alligator

ant

beaver

campfire

Printing and Letter Sounds

Start

Follow the arrows with your finger, then a pencil.

Trace and print B and b. Say the letter sound.

2

B 3

B B B B B B B

B

1

b 2

b b b b b b b b

b

Circle the things that start with b.

bear

balloon

tree

book

ball

boat

Printing and Letter Sounds

Follow the arrows with your finger, then a pencil.

Trace and print C and c. Say the letter sound.

C C C C C C C C C C

C

C C C C C C C C C C C

c

Circle the things that start with c.

candle   car   fish   carrot

Printing and Letter Sounds

Follow the arrows with your finger, then a pencil.

Trace and print D and d. Say the letter sound.

Circle the things that start with d.

dog

deer

house

dime

dinosaur

polar bear

Printing and Letter Sounds

Follow the arrows with your finger, then a pencil.

Start

Trace and print E and e. Say the letter sound.

Colour things that start with e.

egg

elephant

butterfly

ear

Printing and Letter Sounds

Follow the arrows with your finger, then a pencil.

Trace and print F and f. Say the letter sound.

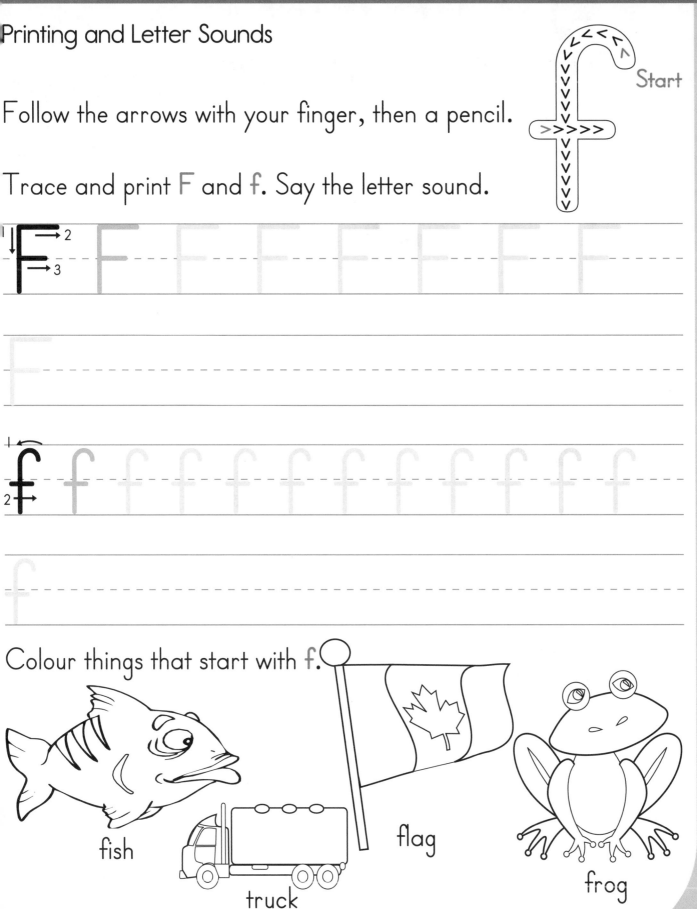

Colour things that start with f.

fish

truck

flag

frog

Review a–f

Draw a line from the picture to the letter it starts with.
Print the letter.

a

f ⨍

c

b

e

d

Printing and Letter Sounds

Start

Follow the arrows with your finger, then a pencil.

Trace and print G and g. Say the letter sound.

G G G G G G G G G

G

g g g g g g g g g g

g

Circle the things that start with g.

goat   gloves   goldfish   sun

Printing and Letter Sounds

Follow the arrows with your finger, then a pencil.

Trace and print H and h. Say the letter sound.

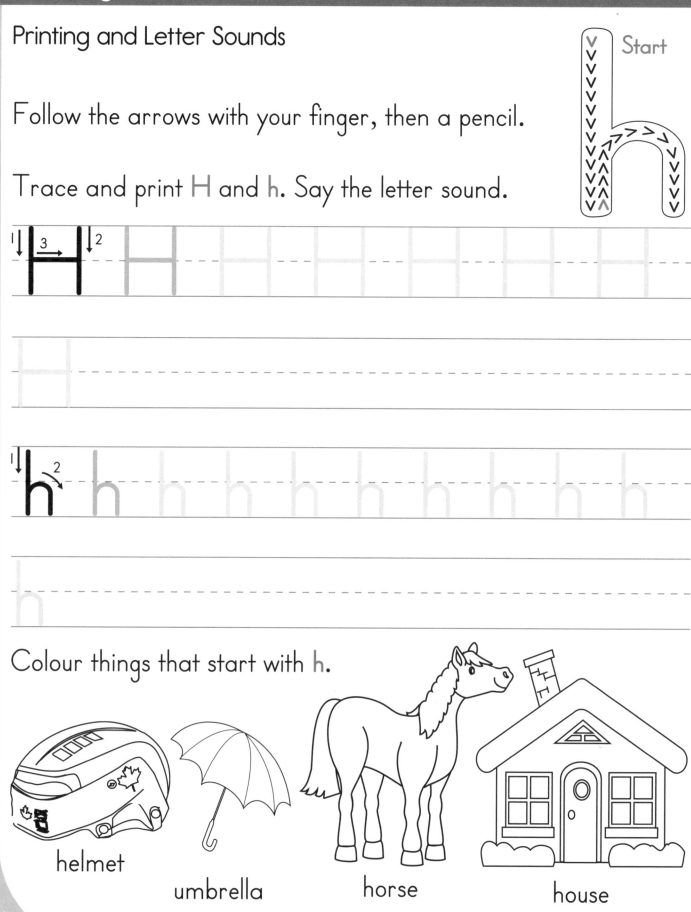

Colour things that start with h.

helmet

umbrella

horse

house

Printing and Letter Sounds

Follow the arrows with your finger, then a pencil.

Start

Trace and print I and i. Say the letter sound.

Circle the things that start with i.

iron

insect

inukshuk

pizza

ice cream

icicles

igloo

Printing and Letter Sounds

 Start

Follow the arrows with your finger, then a pencil.

Trace and print J and j. Say the letter sound.

J J J J J J J J J J J J

J

j j j j j j j j j j j j j j

j

Circle the things that start with j.

juggle

jam

calculator

jack-o-lantern

juice

jacket

Printing and Letter Sounds

Start

Follow the arrows with your finger, then a pencil.

Trace and print K and k. Say the letter sound.

K K K K K K K K

K

k k k k k k k k k

k

Circle the things that start with k.

keys

kite

apple

ambulance

grapes

Printing and Letter Sounds

Start

Follow the arrows with your finger, then a pencil.

Trace and print L and l. Say the letter sound.

Circle the things that start with l.

leaf

bee

lemon

lamp

lock

ladder

18

Review g–l

Draw a line from the picture to the letter it starts with.
Print the letter.

g

i

j

h   h

l

k

Printing and Letter Sounds

Follow the arrows with your finger, then a pencil.

Start

Trace and print M and m. Say the letter sound.

M M M M M M M M

M

m m m m m m m m

m

Draw 2 things that start with m.

moose   mouse

Printing and Letter Sounds

Start

Follow the arrows with your finger, then a pencil.

Trace and print N and n. Say the letter sound.

Draw 2 things that start with n.

nuts   net

21

Printing and Letter Sounds

Start

Follow the arrows with your finger, then a pencil.

Trace and print O and o. Say the letter sound.

Colour things that start with o.

orange

kite

off and on

olive

owl

Printing and Letter Sounds

Start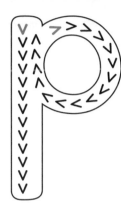

Follow the arrows with your finger, then a pencil.

Trace and print P and p. Say the letter sound.

P P P P P P P P P P

P

p p p p p p p p p p p

p

Colour the things that start with p.

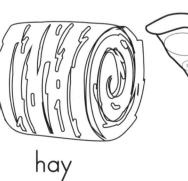

hay

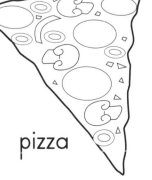

pizza

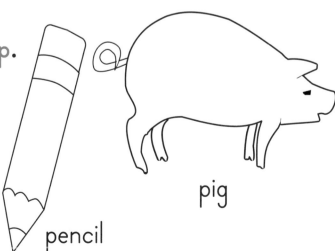

pencil

pig

23

Printing and Letter Sounds

Follow the arrows with your finger, then a pencil.

Trace and print Q and q. Say the letter sound.

Circle the things that start with q.

quarter

truck

queen

goose

quilt

Printing and Letter Sounds

Follow the arrows with your finger, then a pencil.

Trace and print R and r. Say the letter sound.

Start

 R R R R R R R

R

r r r r r r r r r r r

r

Circle the things that start with r.

raspberries   rock   bear   radish

Review m–r

Draw a line from the picture to the letter it starts with.
Print the letter.

m

o   O

q

n

r

p

Printing and Letter Sounds

Follow the arrows with your finger, then a pencil.

Trace and print S and s. Say the letter sound.

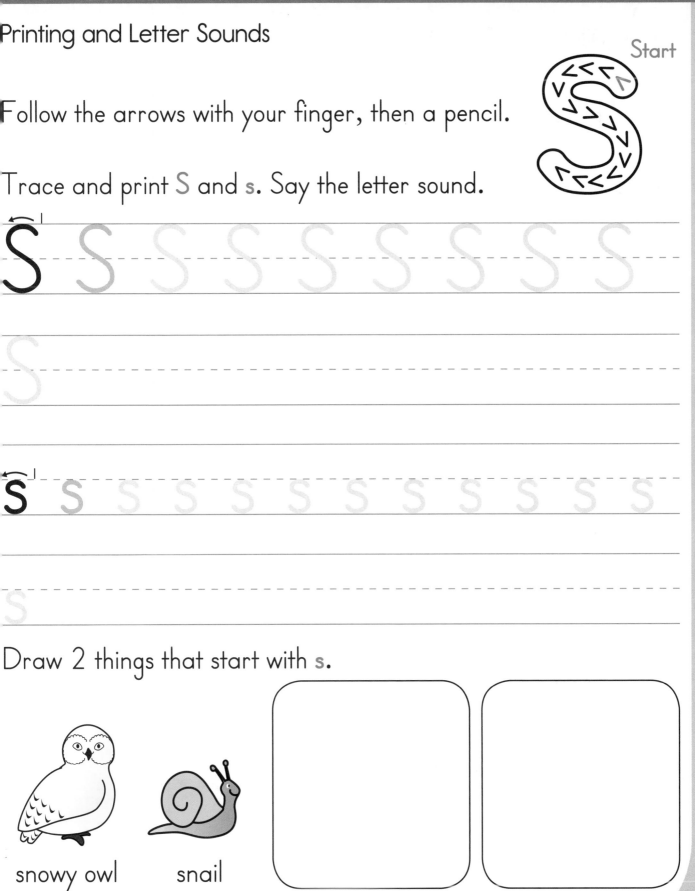

Draw 2 things that start with s.

snowy owl   snail

Printing and Letter Sounds

Follow the arrows with your finger, then a pencil.

Trace and print T and t. Say the letter sound.

Start

Colour the things that start with t.

teapot   table   tree   boat

Printing and Letter Sounds

Start

Follow the arrows with your finger, then a pencil.

Trace and print U and u. Say the letter sound.

Put a ✔ on things that start with u.

up

UP

umbrella

apple

unicorn

uniform

arm

toy

Printing and Letter Sounds

Start

Follow the arrows with your finger, then a pencil.

Trace and print V and v. Say the letter sound.

Put a ✔ on things that start with v.

violin

train

vest

vacuum

fingerprint

volcano

vase

30

Printing and Letter Sounds

Follow the arrows with your finger, then a pencil.

Trace and print W and w. Say the letter sound.

Start

Colour the things that start with w.

wagon

worm

watch

rabbit

watermelon

Printing and Letter Sounds

Start

Follow the arrows with your finger, then a pencil.

Trace and print X and x. Say the letter sound.

Colour the things that start or end with x.

socks

six

x-ray

xylophone

box

32

Review s–x

Draw a line from the picture to the letter it starts with.
Print the letter.

s _____

u _____

w W _____

v _____

x _____

t _____

Printing and Letter Sounds

Start

Follow the arrows with your finger, then a pencil.

Trace and print Y and y. Say the letter sound.

Colour the things that start with y.

yolk

yo-yo

honey

yarn

yellow paint

Printing and Letter Sounds

Start

Follow the arrows with your finger, then a pencil.

Trace and print Z and z. Say the letter sound.

Circle the things that start with z.

O
zero

zigzag

zebra

zoo

zipper

stroller

sun

Alphabetical Order Maze

Follow the alphabet path with your finger then a pencil.
Try not to touch the sides or the letters!

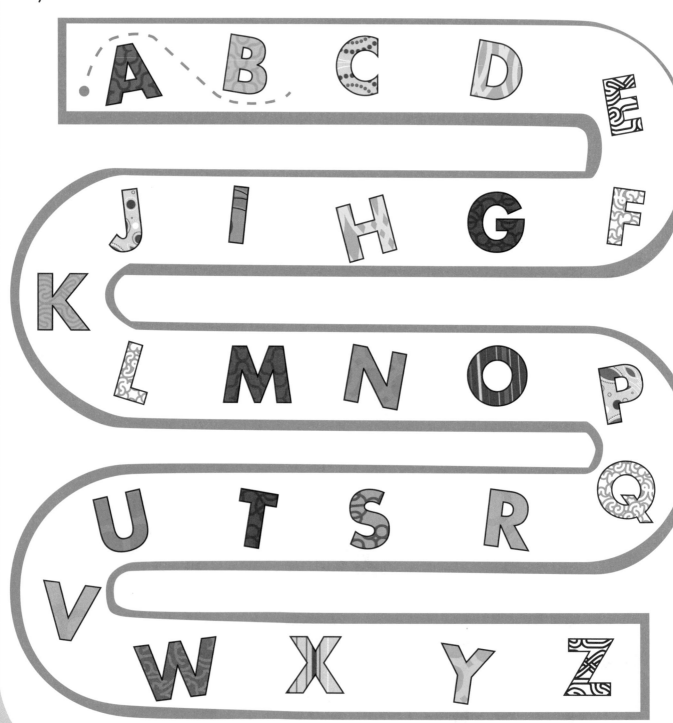

Use a pencil to follow the dots from a to z.
Colour the picture.

Start

Alphabet Review

Circle the beginning letter.

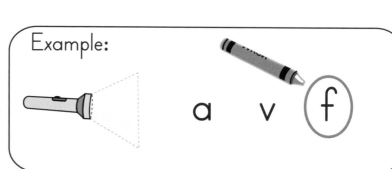

Example:

a   v   (f)

d   a   w

b   t   m

p   j   r

i   p   l

a   s   t

b   j   n

Alphabet Review

Circle the beginning letter.

Example:

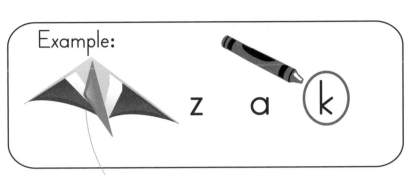

z   a   (k)

d   l   a

g   p   s

v   t   f

b   d   g

o   a   h

w   u   f

Alphabet Review

Example:

Print the first letter.

c e h r m d

m

40

Alphabet Review

Print the first letter.

q u j z w v y x

Example:

_____

z

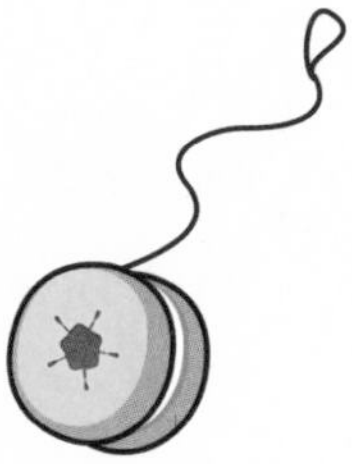

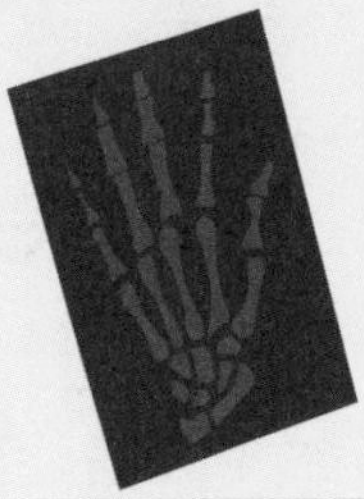

_____

_____

_____

_____

_____

_____

_____

Rhyme Time

Rhyming words start with different sounds and end with the same sound. Draw a line to each rhyming pair.

hat   house

mouse   three   3

tree   pan

pie   frog

fan   cat

log   tie

pen   car

jar   ten   10

Rhyme Time

Read the words from the rhyming word families.

at

sat
cat
hat
mat
rat
pat

ap

cap
map
lap
nap
tap
gap

en

den
pen
men
hen
ten

an

can
man
fan
tan
ran
van

et

pet
get
wet
met
let
yet

ut

but
cut
hut
nut
gut
rut

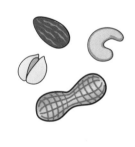

in

pin
tin
win
fin
bin
din

ot

dot
got
hot
not
pot
lot

it

hit
pit
sit
bit
fit
kit

Rhyme Time

Make rhyming words by adding the letter on the left to the pair of letters on the right. Say each word.

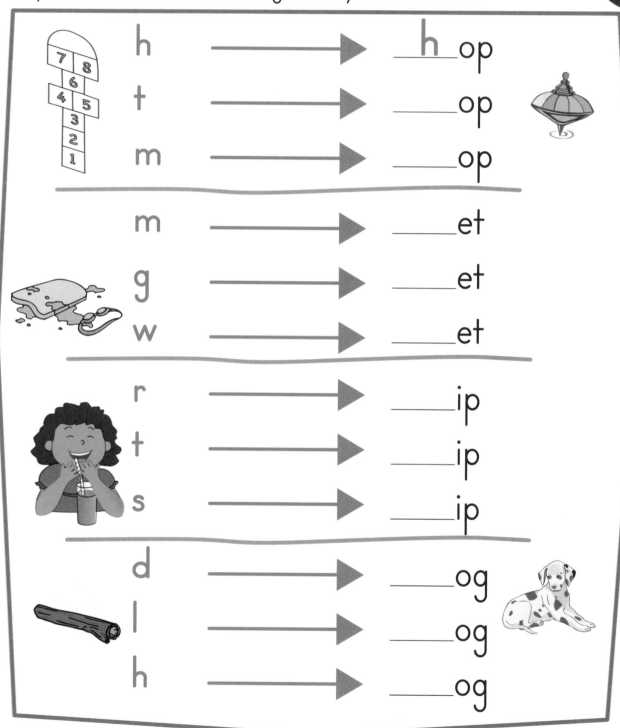

h   ⟶   __h__ op

t   ⟶   ___ op

m   ⟶   ___ op

m   ⟶   ___ et

g   ⟶   ___ et

w   ⟶   ___ et

r   ⟶   ___ ip

t   ⟶   ___ ip

s   ⟶   ___ ip

d   ⟶   ___ og

l   ⟶   ___ og

h   ⟶   ___ og

Super Sight Words

Here are some words to help you write stories.
Print each word.
Draw a line to the matching word.

a   a   my

am   I

I   a

is   at

at   am

my   is

More Super Sight Words

Here are some more words to help write stories.

Print each word.

Draw a line to the matching word.

and   and   you

see   me

me   look

to   see

look   and

you   to

I Can Write Sentences

Look at the picture. Read and print the sentence.

I see my house.

- -

Look at the cake.

- -

I Can Write Sentences

Look at the picture. Read and print the sentence.

I am playing at the park.

I see you and me.

I Can Write Sentences

Look at the picture. Read the sentence and fill in the missing letters. Print the sentence.

I see a d____ and a c____.

_____

- - - - - - - - - - - - - - - - - -

_____

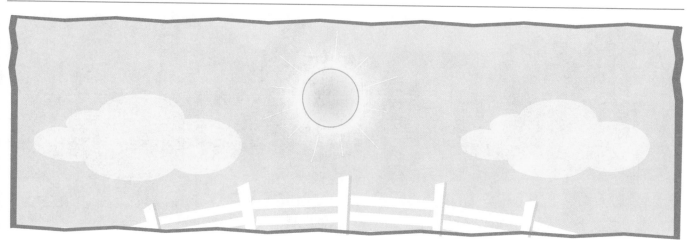

The s____ is in t____ sky.

_____

- - - - - - - - - - - - - - - - - -

_____

I Can Write Sentences

Look at the picture. Read the sentence and fill in the missing letters. Print the sentence.

The boat ___ ___ on ___ ___ ___ ___ lake.

T___ ___ ___ bird is up ___ ___ ___ the tree.

All About Me

Write about you. Draw pictures to match.

This is me!

I am _____ years old.

This is where I live!

My address is _____

_____

ut My Family

rite about your family. Draw a picture to match.

About My Family!

There are _____ people in my family.
Here are their names.

_____

_____

_____

_____

_____

_____

_____

_____

A Letter

Write a letter to someone special. Then draw a picture.

_____

Dear _____ ,

_____

_____

_____

_____

_____

_____

Please write back to me.

From,

_____

A Shopping List

It is time to go shopping.
Make a list to tell what you want to buy.

milk

eggs

bananas

apple

Grocery List

_____

_____

_____

_____

_____

_____

_____

_____

_____

_____

_____

_____

_____

cereal

carrots

broccoli

grapes

...A Story

Write about your favourite thing to do. Draw a picture.

My Favourite Thing to Do

I like to

_____

_____

_____

_____

_____

_____

...A Story

Write about a fun summer day. Draw a picture.

A Fun Summer Day

...A Story

Write about a fun fall day. Draw a picture.

A Fun Fall Day

...A Story

Write about a fun winter day. Draw a picture.

A Fun Winter Day

_____

_____

_____

_____

_____

_____

_____

_____

...A Story

Write about a fun spring day. Draw a picture.

A Fun Spring Day

Solutions

Page 6

Page 7

Page 8

Page 9

Page 10

Page 11

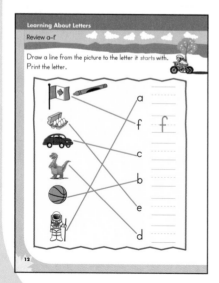

Page 12

Page 13

Page 14

Solutions

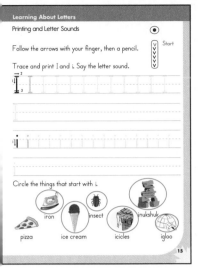

Page 15

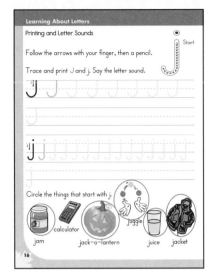

Page 16

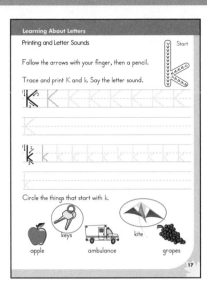

Page 17

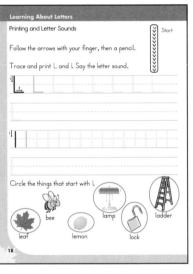

Page 18

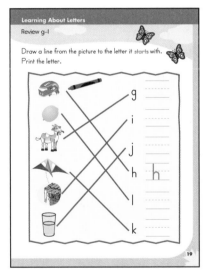

Page 19

Page 20

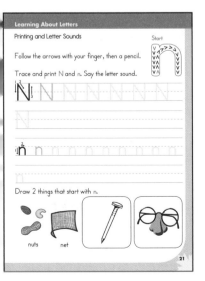

Page 21

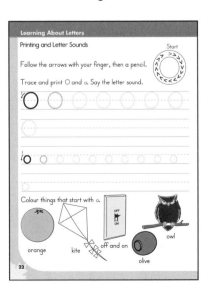

Page 22

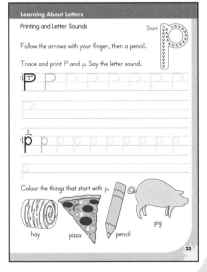

Page 23

Solutions

Page 24

Page 25

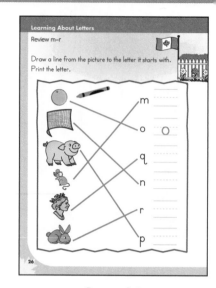

Page 26

Page 27

Page 28

Page 29

Page 30

Page 31

Page 32

Solutions

Page 33

Page 34

Page 35

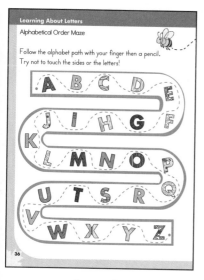

Page 36

Page 37

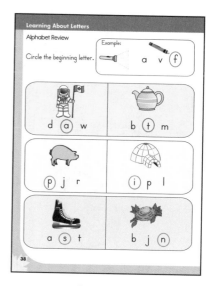

Page 38

Page 39

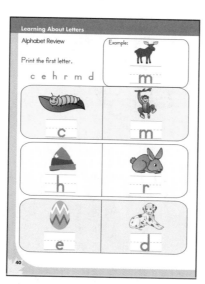

Page 40

Page 41

Solutions

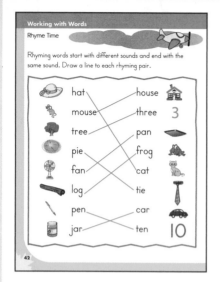

Page 42

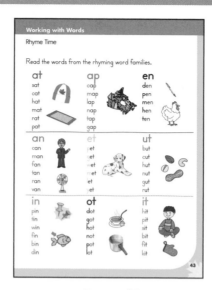

Page 43

Page 44

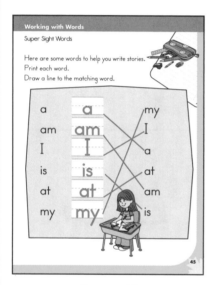

Page 45

Page 46

Page 49

Page 50

You are done!

64